For Danielle and Matthew
—G.H.
To Kelsey
—D.C.

Text copyright © 1995 by Gail Herman.
Illustrations copyright © 1995 by Doug Cushman.
All rights reserved. Published by Scholastic Inc.
Printed in the U.S.A.

ISBN 0-439-45168-X

15 14   40   11 10

Teddy Bear for Sale

by Gail Herman
Illustrated by Doug Cushman

SCHOLASTIC INC.

Cartwheel
B·O·O·K·S ®

New York   Toronto   London   Auckland   Sydney
Mexico City   New Delhi   Hong Kong   Buenos Aires

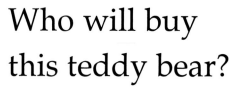

Who will buy
this teddy bear?

Not this girl.
She wants a big red ball.

Not this boy.
He wants a bat.

This girl wants a paint set.

This boy wants a truck.

"Nobody wants me,"
the teddy bear says.
"So I will run away!"

Down the bear jumps!

He jumps into a car.
Off he goes.

The bear drives to a boat

and the boat sets sail.

The bear sails to a train.

The train chugs away.

He stops by a skate

and the skate rolls along.

Then he rolls to a slide.

Down the bear goes!

Down, down, down . . .

then up, up, up!

Over the skate,
the train, the boat,

and the car.

Over the girls
and over the boys.

Plop!
He lands back on the counter.

"Wow!" says a boy.
"What a great bear!"

Who will buy this teddy bear?

"I will!"
says the boy…

and he takes the bear home.